FLYING MY KITE
AN EARLY READER SERIES
READER 4

Authors:
Annie Brown
Alpha Omega Staff

804 N. 2nd Ave. E.
Rock Rapids, IA 51246-1759

Instant Words

1.	the	he	go	who
2.	a	I	see	an
3.	is	they	then	their
4.	you	one	us	she
5.	to	good	no	new
6.	and	me	him	said
7.	we	about	by	did
8.	that	had	was	boy
9.	in	if	come	three
10.	not	some	get	down
11.	for	up	or	work
12.	at	her	two	put
13.	with	do	man	were
14.	it	when	little	before
15.	on	so	has	just
16.	can	my	them	long

17.	will	very	how	here
18.	are	all	like	other
19.	of	would	our	old
20.	this	any	what	take
21.	your	been	know	cat
22.	as	out	make	again
23.	but	there	which	give
24.	be	from	much	after
25.	have	day	his	many
26.	shepherd	there'll	comes	show
27.	judges	looking	children	hanky
28.	hello	among	friend	goes
29.	weather	bears	cocoa	zebra
30.	summer	parachute		

Sisters

My sister helps me every day.

She may brush my hair or make my bed.

She may play a game with me.

She may wait to help me so that I won't be late.

She may tell me tales at the end of the day.

She may help me to obey.
I may give her a hug to say "Thank you."

Waiting for Grandma

"How long do we have to wait until Grandma Joan gets here?" cried Julie.

"I don't know," replied Aunt Sue. "It isn't safe for her plane to fly in the rain, so her flight has been delayed."

"Do you think it will be more than five minutes?" Julie asked. "It's been over three years since I've seen her. I can't wait much longer."

"I want to see Grandma Joan, too," answered Aunt Sue. "But I can't make the rain stop, so we will both have to be patient."

"What can I do while I wait?" Julie was trying to be patient, but it wasn't easy.

"Why don't you paint a picture for Grandma Joan? You can give it to her when she arrives," suggested Aunt Sue.

"I like that idea. It will keep me busy, and the time will go faster. Thanks, Aunt Sue," exclaimed Julie with a big smile. "You have the best ideas!"

Julie's Painting

Julie spent the next hour painting a picture for Grandma Joan. It was something very special. It was a beautiful rainbow with bright colors. Red was on top, then orange, yellow, green, blue, and purple on the bottom.

Julie liked rainbows. Every time it rained, she would run outside to look for one in the sky. Rainbows made her smile. She hoped her painting of a rainbow would make Grandma Joan smile, too.

Later in the afternoon, Grandma Joan called and said she was waiting at the airport for someone to pick her up. Julie was so excited. Now she didn't have to wait any longer. Now she could give Grandma Joan her painting of a rainbow.

When they arrived at the airport, Julie could see Grandma Joan waiting by a bench with her suitcases.

"There she is!" cried Julie.

Julie raced down the sidewalk to meet Grandma Joan. They gave each other a big bear hug.

"I'm so happy to see you," Grandma Joan said. "I've waited so long."

"Me, too," replied Julie as she gave her grandma the painting of the rainbow.

Grandma Joan smiled, just like Julie hoped she would.

Then they both looked up at the sky. The sun was shining through the clouds now, and in the distance was a rainbow as beautiful as Julie's painting.

Sheep

The sheep are happy.
The shepherd will feed them.
He will keep them safe.
He will not let them walk on steep hills.
He will need to check the feet of the sheep.
He will find a nice place for them to sleep.
The sheep act silly and funny,
but the shepherd will take care of them.

Steven and Taylor

Steven is eleven, and Taylor is three.

Steven likes to play games like "Find the Object" with his little brother. First he'll decide on an object. Then he will hide it. He gives clues to Taylor so he can find it.

Sometimes when they play this game, Taylor finds the object right away. Steven thinks Taylor is pretty smart for only being three.

After the brothers are done playing the game, Steven fixes a snack for both of them. It might be crackers and cheese with milk to drink or a piece of fruit.

"Today the snack is green grapes," he tells Taylor.

"I like gween gwapes," says Taylor grinning. He puts them in his blue pail and runs to the back door.

Steven always laughs when he hears Taylor say "gween gwapes."

"Someday he'll say it right," he tells himself.

"Can I eat these outside?" Taylor asks Steven. It was a sunny day and just right for sitting in the soft grass.

"It's okay with me," answered Steven. "Please stay in our yard."

A few minutes later, Steven peeked out the window to check on Taylor. He had fallen asleep on the grass next to his blue pail of green grapes.

"Hmmmm," thought Steven with a smile. "Maybe tomorrow we'll have 'waisins' for a snack."

What Do You Want to Be?

"I want to drive a train when I grow up," Shane told his friend James.

"I would drive down the railroad tracks. I would wave to the people as I pass by. I would blow the train whistle so they can hear it from miles away."

"It would be fun to ride on a train," said James, "but I would rather fly an airplane. I would race down the runway and take off high into the sky. I would wave my wings up and down to say hello to the people on the ground."

Casey saw his younger brother Shane talking to James and came over to join them. "What are you two talking about?" he asked.

"We're talking about what we want to be when we grow up," answered Shane. "I want to drive a train and James wants to fly airplanes."

"What do you want to be, Casey?" James asked.

"I want to be a teacher," Casey told them.

"A teacher?" they both said at the same time.

"Why do you want to be a teacher? It doesn't seem like much fun." James asked him.

"Well," Casey replied. "Do you know how to drive a train or fly an airplane? Someone has to teach you. I want to be a teacher so I can learn about all kinds of things and teach others. It will be lots of fun."

The boys looked at each other and shook their heads.

"Woo, woo, chug-a-chug," said Shane the train driver.

"Zoom, zoom," said James the airplane pilot, as they both raced out the door.

Surprise! Surprise!

It's Lila's birthday. Let's have a surprise party.

"I'll bring a cake," said May. "It'll be a big one."

"I'll bring the ice cream," said Mike. "There'll be lots of it."

Here comes Lila. Surprise! Surprise! Happy birthday, Lila!

Casey's First Lesson

Casey sat on the steps watching James and Shane play. Shane was driving a train, and James was flying an airplane.

"They know the actions," he thought, "but what do they really know about trains or airplanes?"

He wanted to tell them they couldn't just climb in and go. They had to learn what to do.

"I'll have to come up with a plan to get them interested in learning," Casey thought to himself. "That's what a teacher would do."

He got on his bike and went to the library. There he looked for books on airplanes and trains. After he checked them out, he went home to read. He chose to sit on the steps outside so the boys would see what he was doing.

"What are you doing?" Shane finally asked.

"Oh, reading," Casey told him.

"What are you reading about?" James asked.

"Oh, just about airplanes and trains. But you wouldn't think it was fun," Casey said in a teasing manner.

The boys looked at each other. This time they didn't run off. They stayed!

"Could we maybe look at one book?" James asked.

"Sure," Casey replied. "If you decide it's a little fun, you can look at the rest, too."

Two hours later, the boys were still sitting on the steps reading books and talking about trains and airplanes.

"Hmmm," Casey said to himself with a smile. "Teaching is fun."

The Pet Show

Diane and Brian are at the pet show.
Diane has her pet rabbit.
Brian has his pet kitten.

Many other children have their pets.
The judges are looking at the pets.
Among the pets are dogs, cats,
fish, rabbits, and birds.

Who will get the First Prize?
What do you think?
Which pet will get the First Prize?

Going to Florida

"We're going to Florida for our vacation this year," Mother and Dad told the family.

"Hurray!" everyone yelled.

Everyone, that is, except seven-year-old Gretchen. She looked pale, but no one noticed right away.

"The beaches in Florida have fine, white sand. We can build great sand castles and play in the ocean," Dad told them.

"If we have time, we'll go down the coast. We might even see a rocket take off," Mother added.

Everyone was excited, except Gretchen.
"I don't want to go to Florida," she cried.
Tears rolled down her cheeks and her body
was shaking.

"What is the matter?" Mother asked. "Why are you so frightened about going to Florida?"

"I heard about Florida from Joey," she said. "He said there are alligators everywhere. Joey said alligators eat people, especially little children."

Mother understood Gretchen's fear and held her tight.

"How about if we get some books about alligators and find out if what Joey says is true," Dad suggested.

"Okay," said Gretchen wiping her tears. "Let's get some books, right now."

Flying My Kite

I made a kite with a long tail.
My friend Tim will help me fly it.
We'll take it up on the hill.

Here comes the wind.
Run with the kite, Tim!
Tim runs very fast.
He lets the kite go.

Up it goes.
Up, up, up.
My kite is flying.
Fly high, kite! Fly high!

The Lazy Little Train

Little Train was lazy.
He didn't like to work.

One day he said,
"I'll not go to work at all."
So Little Train sat.
He sat and sat and sat.

Soon Little Train said,
"This isn't fun at all.
I'll go to work."
Now he isn't a lazy little train.

No More Alligator Fear

Gretchen's fear about alligators got the whole family interested in learning about them. They all decided they would go to the library after lunch. It would be a family adventure.

The library was new and close to home. So Mother said, "Why don't we walk? It's a nice day, and the exercise will be good for everyone."

Gretchen had never been to the new library. When she walked in, she saw books everywhere.

"There are so many," she said. "How will we ever find books on alligators?" Her big brother Alan took her by the hand and showed how to use the computer to look up subjects. He typed in "alligators" and the screen came up with book titles and numbers.

"See this number?" he told her. "It tells us where to find books on alligators."

Alan wrote the numbers down on a small piece of paper. Gretchen followed him to the shelves, and together they found books about alligators.

Gretchen didn't like the pictures of the huge creatures with big eyes.

"They do have a big mouth," she thought. "Maybe Joey was right."

Just then, Alan said, "Look, it says right here in this book, 'Alligators usually do not harm humans.'"

As they read more, Gretchen's fears went away. "I can't wait to tell Joey," she said. "Then we're all going to Florida."

"Hurray!" everyone said quietly. Everyone, including Gretchen.

Friends

The girls will put their school books away.
They will get the lunches.
The apple looks good!
The orange looks good!
Ann looks at Sue's orange.
Pam will eat her sandwich.
Soon lunch will end.
The girls will take their books to the classroom.

A Little about Alligators

Gretchen learned a lot about alligators at the library.

She didn't have to be afraid that an alligator would come after her, but like any wild animal, she learned to leave them alone. The more facts she read, the better she felt. Gretchen also realized that some of the information Joey told her was true.

"Listen to this," she told Alan. "Alligators do live in Florida, but they aren't everywhere. They like swamps, lakes, and rivers. They are mostly found in the Everglades which is in the southern part of the state. Sometimes alligators are found in places where people live, too."

"There's a good chance of seeing one if we go to the right places," Alan told her.

"I also found out alligators are the biggest reptile alive today," she read on. "When they are babies, they are only 8 to 10 inches long, but some adults can grow to be over 20 feet long. That's longer than our minivan!"

"Now I know alligators don't eat people, but what do they eat?" Gretchen asked her brother.

"Well, it says in this book alligators are not picky eaters," Alan explained. "They eat just about any insect or small animal they can catch. Some of their favorites are fish, softshell turtles, water snakes, and nesting birds."

"I think I will check these books out so I can read more at home," Gretchen told Alan. "I guess I would like to see an alligator when we get to Florida, but I wouldn't want to get too close. Do you think they have an alligator zoo?"

Joan's New School

Joan wasn't very happy.
She didn't like her new school.
She didn't know any of the children.

The children told Joan their names.
They asked her to play with them.
They worked and played all day.

Quite soon it was time to go home.
Joan is happy now.
She likes her new school, and
she has many new friends.

The Bee Chase

"Help, help," cried Trudy. "I think a bee is chasing me!"

Quickly, Mother opened the door and Trudy ran in the house.

"That was close," she said. "That mean bee almost stung me!"

"Bees don't usually bother us," said Mother. "Why was this bee chasing you?" she asked.

"I don't know," said Trudy quietly. "Where do you think the queen bee is?" she asked, changing the subject.

"Never mind about the queen. Are you sure you don't know why it chased you?" Mother asked again.

"Well, I was just looking at the flowers in Bobby's yard," said Trudy. "I wanted to pick the yellow one. It was the one the bee was sitting on so I shooed the bee away."

"I see," said Mother.

"I guess I made the bee mad," said Trudy.

"I agree," replied Mother. "Next time you'll know."

"Yes, I will," said Trudy. "Next time I will let the bee be!"

Mother smiled. She knew Trudy had learned her lesson.

"Oh, Mom," Trudy said. "I almost forgot. This is for you."

Baby Zebra

Baby Zebra had a bad cold. He sneezed.

AH CHOO!

Mother Zebra gave him a hanky.
Baby Zebra sneezed again.

AH CHOO!

The hanky went up, up, up. Then it came

down,
down,
down.

Baby Zebra clapped his hooves.

"Look, Mother," he said, "look at my funny parachute!"

Playing

Hello.
Is this Jeanie?
This is Dee Dee.
Will you come and play with me?

I have a new bike.
It is blue and white.
We can go for a ride.

Oh, good!
I will see you soon.
Goodbye.

Busy Bees

Bees are hard workers. They live together in a group called a colony. The home they build is a hive. The hive is made up of hundreds of combs. The combs are made out of wax. Each comb is perfect. It has six sides and is open on one end.

The combs are used for many different jobs. Some store food, others hold eggs until they hatch, and others are like bedrooms for some of the bees.

The female bees are called worker bees. They do everything for the hive. They care for the queen, the eggs, and the male bees. They build the waxy combs, collect pollen and nectar from flowers, and stand guard over the hive. Most of bees in a hive are worker bees.

There is so much to do, and they are busy all the time. Without the worker bees, the hive would not survive.

The queen bee is bigger than all the rest. There is only one queen in each hive.

The queen has only one job. She lays the eggs. She may lay hundreds of eggs in one day. After she finishes, she rests. The worker bees feed her and care for her.

The male bees are called drones. They are chubby and have the biggest eyes. They don't do much of anything. Their only job is to mate with the queen bee. Once they do this, they die.

If anyone ever says to you, "My, you're busy as a bee today!" you will know they are talking about a worker bee, the busiest bee of all.

Leaves

Some trees have leaves.
In the summer, it is hot.
The leaves are green.
The leaves make food for the tree.
In the fall, it gets cold.
The leaves are yellow, red, and brown.
They fall from the tree.
Soon the tree has no leaves on it.
We put the leaves in big piles
and jump into them.

The Quilt

Mrs. Sanders rang the doorbell.

"Hello, Mrs. Sanders. What do you have in the box?" Melissa asked.

"This box is filled with fabric squares. There are many colors and different patterns on each square," she told Melissa.

"What are you going to do with them?" Melissa asked reaching for the squares on the top.

"Your mother and I are going to make a quilt. We will stitch the squares together one at a time. When it is finished, it will be big enough to put on a small bed," she answered with a smile.

"Is it going to be for someone?" Melissa wanted to know.

"We haven't made up our minds yet," Mrs. Sanders said as she put the box on the table. "It will take a long time to make, so we don't have to choose who we will give it to just yet."

Melissa hoped it would be for her. She picked through the fabric and showed Mrs. Sanders her favorite squares.

Every afternoon, Mrs. Sanders would come over to work on the quilt with Melissa's mother. Melissa would sit for hours watching as each square was stitched together.

At night, Melissa would dream of the beautiful quilt. She could see it laying neatly on her bed. Oh, how she hoped it would be for her. She knew she would have to be patient, though, because making a quilt takes a long, long time.

I Am Always with You

Andrew loves going to the big field behind his house. He goes every afternoon when he gets home from school. He likes to look for the gray squirrels that live in the woods nearby, but he never goes far from the field.

Sometimes Andrew gives the squirrels names. Squirt is the name he gave the littlest one. Squirmy is the one that never stands still for more than two seconds.

He likes to watch the squirrels run up and down the trees and gather seeds they find on the ground. Once in a while, they chase each other like a game of tag.

One afternoon, Andrew was watching his squirrel friends play their game of tag. "They are so funny," he thought as he followed them into the woods.

He didn't realize he had gone so far until it began to rain. He looked around and saw trees all around him. He didn't know which way would take him back to the field.

Andrew looked for shelter but couldn't find anything that would protect him. He was lost and getting wet, but for some reason he wasn't afraid.

Thinking about what he should do, Andrew put his hands in his pockets to keep them warm. In one pocket, he felt a piece of paper. He pulled it out and looked at it. It was his Bible memory verse for the week. He had put it in his pocket so he would remember to practice it often. It read, "I am with you always. Matthew 28:20."

Andrew felt a sense of peace come over him. Now he knew why he wasn't afraid. He knew Jesus would keep him safe.

Snow

Snow has fallen on the tops of the hills.
It will stay as long as the weather is cold.
The birds have gone for the winter.
They will stay as long as the weather is cold.
Ice has formed on the lake.
It will stay as long as the weather is cold.
Bears are sleeping in caves.
They will stay as long as the weather is cold.
Children are inside drinking cocoa.
They will stay as long as the weather is cold.

NOTES

NOTES

NOTES

NOTES

NOTES